Attic Book
of
Special Days
for Women

First published in 1990 by
Attic Press
44 East Essex Street
Dublin 2

Cover Design: Luly Mason
Origination: Attic Press
Printing: Norhaven

Compiled by Róisín Conroy, Michelle Cullen,
Margaret Neylon and Ailbhe Smyth.

The illustrations used throughout are from
early 20th Century Italian sources.

You wrote me a lovely letter on my 90th birthday.
What I have done looks small to me, but I have tried
a good deal for the best I have known ... don't you
think that the best things in life are already in view?
The opportunities for women, the growing toleration
and sympathy in religion, the sacred cause of peace?
I have lived like Moses, to see the entrance into the
Promised Land. How much is this to be thankful
for!

Julia Ward Howe
Letter to Mrs Spofford 1909

January

JANUARY *1*

NANCY LOPES Golfing Champion, born USA 1957
GRETTA BOWEN Artist, born Ireland 1800

New Year's Day

1 January 1961
Birth Control Pill
launched in England.

JANUARY *2*

We turn not older with the years but newer with every day.
Emily Dickinson, USA

JANUARY 3

SONIA KOWALEWSKY
Mathematician, born Russia 1850

_____

_____

_____

_____

_____

JANUARY 4

JANE WYMAN (Sarah Jane Faulks)
Film Actress, born USA 1914

DYAN CANNON (Samile Diane Friesen)
Film Actress, born USA 1937

_____

_____

_____

_____

_____

*I was able to snatch a few precious days in January to write
undisturbed. But when shall I ever be so fortunate again as to
break a foot?*

Florence Price, USA

I praise loudly; I blame softly.
Catherine II of Russia

LORETTA YOUNG (Gretchen Young)
Film Actress and Oscar winner, born USA 1913

ANNA MARIA HALL Novelist, born Ireland 1800

The Epiphany - also known as Women's Christmas

JANUARY 7

Men fear women's strength.
Anais Nin

JANUARY 8

SHIRLEY BASSEY Singer and Entertainer, born Wales 1937
JULIA GLOVER Actress, born Ireland 1779

*Speak peace and fear and hope and love and pain and sadness
and joy.
Speak it for all of us who left our shoes at the school door.*
Monique Griffiths, UK

SIMONE DE BEAUVOIR
Writer, Philosopher and Activist, born France 1908

GRACIE FIELDS (Grace Stansfield)
Singer and Comedienne, born England 1898

GYPSY ROSE LEE
(Rose Louise Hovick)
Entertainer, born USA
1914

JOAN BAEZ
Folk Singer, born USA
1941

BARBARA HEPWORTH
Abstract Sculptor, born England 1903

Change your life today. Don't gamble on the future, act now without delay.

Simone de Beauvoir, France

JANUARY *11*

AMELIA EARHART becomes the first woman to make a solo
flight across the Pacific Ocean, 1935.

JANUARY *12*

JENNIFER JOHNSTON Writer, born Ireland 1930
MAIRE O'NEILL (Molly Allgood) Actress, born Ireland 1887

I am all impatience till tomorrow evening, the 12th January,
which is our Russian New Year's Eve, in order to test my
fortune in a looking-glass ... Long live the year 1874 in Russia
and farewell 1873!

Marie Bashkirtseff, Russia

JANUARY *13*

SOPHIE TUCKER (Sophia Abusa)
Singer, born Russia 1884

_____

_____

_____

_____

_____

Russian New Year's Day

JANUARY *14*

FAY DUNAWAY
Film Actress and Oscar winner, born USA 1941
TILLIE OLSEN
Writer, born USA 1913

_____

_____

_____

_____

_____

I've been rich and I've been poor - rich is better.
Sophie Tucker, USA

JANUARY *15*

Perhaps a child, like a cat, is so much inside herself that she
does not see herself in the mirror.

Anais Nin, USA

15 January 1975
Launch of the United
Nations Women's Year
and Decade.

JANUARY *16*

DIANA WYNYARD (Dorothy Cox)
Actress, born England 1906

SUSAN SONTAG Writer and Critic, born USA 1933

ETHEL MERMAN (Ethel Simmerman) Singer, born USA 1909

ANNE BRONTË Novelist, born England 1820
MOIRA SHEARER (Moira King) Ballerina, born Scotland 1926

_____

_____

_____

_____

_____

I know I'm black. I see it all the time, I like it. I wouldn't want
to wash it off.

Joan Armatrading, USA

_____

_____

_____

_____

_____

*But everybody needs a home so at least you can have some
place to leave which is where most other folks will say you
must be coming from.*

June Jordan, USA

JANUARY *19*

DOLLY PARTON
Country and Western Singer, born USA 1946

PATRICIA HIGHSMITH
Crime Fiction Writer, born UK 1921

JANUARY *20*

PATRICIA NEAL
Film Actress and Oscar winner, born USA 1926

AQUARIUS
20 Jan - 18 Feb
Element: Air
Ruler: Uranus
Friendly; loyal; future oriented;
telepathic; freedom loving; idealistic.

The future is made of the same stuff as the present.
Simone Weil, France

_____

_____

_____

_____

_____

ANN SOTHERN (Harriette Lake)
Film Actress, born USA 1912

_____

_____

_____

_____

_____

JANUARY *23*

I give myself sometimes admirable advice, but I am incapable
of taking it.

Lady Mary Wortley Montague, UK

JANUARY *24*

EDITH WHARTON Writer, born USA 1862

FRANZISKA TIBURTIUS First woman doctor in Germany,
born Germany 1843

VIRGINIA WOOLF (Virginia Stephen)
Writer, born England 1882

EARTHA KITT Singer and Actress, born USA 1928

The older one grows, the more one likes indecency.
Virginia Woolf, England

JANUARY *27*

Give me a dozen such heartbreaks
if that would help me lose a couple of pounds.

Colette, France

_____

_____

_____

_____

_____

Chinese New Year

JANUARY *28*

COLETTE Writer, born France 1873

_____

_____

_____

_____

28 January 1935
Iceland becomes the first
country in the world to
legalise abortion on
medical-social grounds.

_____

*There is no more an age for being a poet than there is for being
in love.*

Colette, France

GERMAINE GREER Writer and Activist, born Australia 1939

VANESSA REDGRAVE Film Actress, born England 1937

30 January 1981
SUSAN HURLEY is the
first woman to be elected
a fellow of All Souls'
College, Oxford since the
foundation of the college
in the 15th century.

JANUARY *31*

ANNA PAVLOVA Prima Ballerina, born Russia 1885
JEAN SIMMONS Film Actress, born England 1929
TERESA DEEVY Playwright, born Ireland 1894

Sometimes I wonder
why the length of my life
is so long

Twisting and turning into those difficult corners
Where problems stand upside down
hiding themselves for fear of finding me.

Joyce Spencer, England

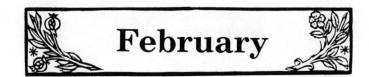

February

Feastday of BRIGID, Celtic goddess and Christian saint

Beginning of Spring (Northern Hemisphere) and
Autumn (Southern Hemisphere)

The ancient Celtic Triple Goddess was later christianised as Saint Brigid when the church was unable to eradicate devotion to her.

NELL GWYN (Eleanor Gwyn)
Actress, born England 1650

Candlemas Day

I was born in the Southern Hemisphere
in the early hours of the dawn
and when I die
I shall return
to a place I call my own.

Meiling Jin, born in Guyana of Chinese parents,
now living in England

FEBRUARY *3*

GERTRUDE STEIN Writer, born USA 1874

ELIZABETH BLACKWELL First woman to qualify as a doctor in the USA, born England 1821

SIMONE WEIL Philosopher, born France 1909

3 February 1981
Dr GRO BRUNDTLAND
is elected Norway's first
woman Prime Minister

FEBRUARY *4*

BETTY FRIEDAN Writer and activist, born USA 1921

IDA LUPINO Film Actress, England, 1918

Considering how dangerous everything is, nothing is really very frightening.

Gertrude Stein, USA and France

By the year 2000 we will, I hope, raise our children to believe
in human potential, not god.

Gloria Steinem, USA

Women first permitted to vote in elections to Parliament
at Westminster, UK, 1918

FEBRUARY 7

DORA BRYAN (Dora Broadbent)
Comedy Actress, born England 1924

_____

_____

_____

7 February 1971
Women in SWITZ-
ERLAND gain the right _____
to vote in an all-male
referendum.

_____

FEBRUARY 8

DAME EDITH EVANS
Shakespearean Actress, born England 1888

PAULA MODERSOHN BECKER Artist, born Germany 1876

_____

_____

_____

_____

_____

*When my mother is working in her flowers she is radiant
almost to the point of being invisible - except as creator: hand
and eye.*

Alice Walker, USA

KATHRYN GRAYSON (Zelma Hedrick)
Actress and Singer, born USA 1923

ALICE WALKER Writer, born USA 1944

JOYCE GRENFELL
Actress and Broadcaster, born England 1910

ROBERTA FLACK Rock Singer, born USA 1939

Feastday of SCHOLASTICA,
patron saint of scholars

FEBRUARY *11*

Together we can hold back the flooding waves.
Ch'in Chin, China

11 February 1852
First public flushing
lavatory for women
opened in London (cost
was 'tuppence' not a
'penny'!)

FEBRUARY *12*

MARY QUANT Fashion Designer, born England 1934
LOU ANDREAS-SALOME
Writer and Psychoanalyst, born Russia 1861

MARIE LLOYD
(Matilda Alice Victoria
Wood) Music hall star,
born England 1870

*You meet your friend, your face brightens - you have struck
gold.*

Kassia, Byzantine Greece

KIM NOVAK (Marilyn Novak)
Film Actress, born USA 1933

MARY SWANZY Artist, born Ireland 1882

Valentine's Day was originally Lupercalia, Roman festival of sexual licence in honour of Juno Februata, the goddess of love.

February 15

CLAIRE BLOOM (Claire Blume)
Film Actress, born England 1931

SUSAN B ANTHONY
Suffragist and Social Reformer, born USA 1882

15 February 1879
Women gain the right
to practice in the
Supreme Court of the
USA.

February 16

To be in love is to touch things with a lighter hand.
Gwendolyn Brooks, USA

Men, their rights and nothing more;
Women, their rights and nothing less.
Susan B Anthony, USA

A kitten is more amusing
than half the people one is obliged to live with.

Lady Sydney Morgan, Ireland

Women of The Americas Day *(Dia de la Mujer de las Americas)*
TONI MORRISON Writer, born USA 1931

Shrove Tuesday, Mardi Gras, or 'Pancake Day', the day before
Lent, the christian period of fasting, occurs about now. This
was New Year's Eve in ancient Rome - a day of feasting and
celebrations before the Day of Atonement on which people
bathed in ashes, a custom which originated in India in honour
of the fire god, Agni.

FEBRUARY *19*

MERLE OBERON (Estelle Marie O'Brien Thompson)
Film Actress, born Tasmania 1911

CARSON McCULLERS Writer, born USA 1917

ADELINA PATTI Opera Singer, born Italy 1843

19 February 1897
The first Women's
Institute founded, in
Canada, by Mrs
Hoodless.

FEBRUARY *20*

One of the nice things nobody ever tells you about middle age
is that it's such a nice change from being young.

Dorothy Canfield Fisher, USA

PISCES 19 Feb - 20 March
Element: Water
Ruler: Neptune and Jupiter
Sensitive; impressionable; compassionate. unconventional;
humorous; creative; mystical side well developed.

'Birth Name' is a term used by feminists as a more accurate
label for the name received at birth than the older term
'maiden name' which has sexual double standard
implications.

Gloria Steinem, USA

EDNA ST VINCENT MILLAY Poet, born USA 1892
JANE BOWLES Writer, born USA 1917

Though Time refeather the wing,
Ankle slip the ring,
The once-confined thing
Is never free again.

Edna St Vincent Millay, USA

FEBRUARY *23*

Waves are circlets of little girls
embracing this world
as they play

Gabriela Mistral, Chile

FEBRUARY *24*

It's not the tragedies that kill us, it's the messes.

Dorothy Parker, USA

24 February 1920
Nancy, Lady Astor, is
the first woman to speak
in the British Parliament
at Westminster.

DAME MYRA HESS
Concert Pianist, born England 1890

_____

_____

_____

_____

_____

25 February 1986
CORAZON AQUINO
becomes President of the
Philippines.

MARGARET LEIGHTON
Stage and Film Actress, born England 1922

_____

_____

_____

_____

_____

I am woman, hear me roar
in numbers too big to ignore
Now I know too much to go back to pretend.

Helen Reddy, Australia

February 27

ELLEN TERRY Actress, born England 1847

JOANNE WOODWARD
Film Actress and Oscar Winner, born USA 1930

ELIZABETH TAYLOR
Film Actress and Oscar Winner, born England 1932

February 28

Happiness is a matter of changing troubles.
Colette, France

ANN LEE Religious Leader, born England 1736

29 February
Leap Year Day.
Occurs every fourth
year.

Black woman out dere you have to Fight back,
Just come forward wid a double attack,
No boder weep
Onno kitchen mat ... Jus Attack.

Nefertiti Gayle, England

Egyptian calendar
The Egyptian calendar was a solar calendar based on a 365-day year of 12 30-day months with 5 days added on at the end.

Julian calendar
The Julian calendar was devised by Julius Caesar as a 12-month year of 31 and 30 days. February would have 29 days but every fourth year (leap year) it would have an extra day.

March

DINAH SHORE Singer, born USA 1921

_____

_____

_____

_____

_____

JENNIFER JONES (Phyllis Isley)
Film Actress and Oscar winner, born USA 1919

KAREN CARPENTER Singer, born USA 1950

_____

_____

_____

_____

_____

MARCH 3

JEAN HARLOW (Harlean Carpenter)
Film Actress, born USA 1911

FATIMA WHITBREAD
Javelin Champion, born England 1961

MARCH 4

It is good to have an end to journey towards; but it is the
journey that matters in the end.

Ursula K Le Guin, USA

*I ask for no favours for my sex. All I ask is that men take their
feet from off our necks.*

Sarah Grimke, USA

ROSA LUXEMBURG
Socialist Activist, born Poland 1871

ELIZABETH BARRET BROWNING Poet, born England 1806

KIRI TE KANAWA Opera Singer, born New Zealand 1944

VALENTINA TERESHKOVA
First woman in space, born Russia 1937

A curse from the depths of womanhood
Is very salt and bitter and good.

Elizabeth Barrett Browning, England

March 7

In the name of the Mother
and of the daughter
and the spirit
of our Grandmothers.

Bernardine Evaristo, England

March 8

International Women's Day *(Dia Internacional de la Mujer)*

In 1857 and 1908 thousands of New York women garment
workers protested against their sweatshop conditions, wages
and right to organise. To commemorate these events, this day
was proclaimed International Women's Day by Clara Zetkin at
the Second International Congress of Socialist Women in
Copenhagen.

VITA SACKVILLE-WEST
Gardener and Writer, born UK 1892

_____

_____

_____

_____

_____

Mothering Sunday, third
Sunday in Lent, occurs
about now.

It is never wise to disregard the sagacity of those who do not
learn their love from books.

Vita Sackville-West, England

_____

_____

_____

_____

_____

Mine eyes have seen the glory of the flame of women's rage,
Kept smouldering for centuries now burning in this age
We no longer will be prisoners in that same gilded cage,
That's why we're marching on.
CHORUS: Glory Glory Halleluja, Glory Glory Halleluja,
Glory Glory Halleluja, for women's time has come.

Women's Freedom Song - Tune: Battle Hymn of the Republic

March *11*

ELEONOR PROCHASKA,
Activist and Freedom Fighter, born Prussia 1785

MADAME d'EPINAY
Writer and Intellectual, born France 1726

March *12*

LISA MINNELLI Entertainer, Film Actress and Oscar winner,
born USA 1946 to actress and singer Judy Garland

---

12 March 1912
Girl Scouts Movement
in America founded by
Juliette Gordon Low.

Mama was just like a beautiful flower that withered and died.
Lisa Minelli

A place for everything and everything in its place.
Mrs Beeton, England

13 March 1957
Women gain the right
to vote in Persia, now
Iran.

MRS ISABELLA BEETON
Cookery Writer, born England 1836

MARCH *15*

LADY GREGORY Playwright, born Ireland 1852
LIDA GUSTAVA HEYMANN
Writer, Educator and Feminist Activist, born Germany 1868

MARCH *16*

Get my swan costume ready.
Anna Pavlova, Russia - her dying words

The future is the view of what is to come which determines the way we act to solve problems in the present.
Margrit Eichler and Hilda Scott

Ramadan begins on this day in 1991,
on 5 March in 1992, on 23 February in 1993.

KATE GREENAWAY
Artist and Illustrator, born England 1846

17 March 1921
The first 'Marie Stopes'
birth control clinic
opened in England.

HARRIET CONSTANCE SMITHSON
Actress, born Ireland 1800

MARCH *19*

MINNA CANTH
Poet and Feminist Activist, born Finland 1844

_____

_____

_____

_____

_____

MARCH *20*

KARIN MICHAELIS
Writer and Feminist Activist, born Denmark 1872

VERA LYNN (Vera Welch)
Singer, born England 1917

_____

_____

_____

_____

20 March
Vernal Equinox (when
day and night are of
equal length)

_____

*By the time your life is finished, you will have learned just
enough to begin it well.*

Eleanor Marx, England

NORA BARNACLE JOYCE
Staunch companion, adored lover,
later married James Joyce,
born Ireland 21 or 22 March 1884

SARAH PURSER Artist, born Ireland 1848

MELASINA TRENCH Writer, born Ireland 1768

Earliest date on which the Christian feast of Easter can fall.

The ancient Festival of Easter honoured the goddess Astarte, the pagan queen of heaven. The hare was sacred to her and was said to lay eggs, symbols of rebirth, for good children on the eve of the feast.

ARIES 21 March - 19 April
Element: Fire
Ruler: Mars
Courageous and bold; initiator of new activities;
adventurous spirit; quick thinker.

MARCH *23*

JOAN CRAWFORD (Lucille Le Sueur)
Film Actress and Dancer, born USA 1908

MARIE BAUM
Socialist Activist and Chemist, born Germany 1874

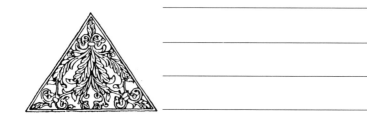

MARCH *24*

FANNY LEWALD
Writer and Feminist Campaigner, born Germany 1811

OLIVE SCHREINER
Writer, born South Africa 1855

If my husband would ever meet a woman on the streets who looked like the women in his paintings, he would fall over in a dead faint.

Madame Picasso, Spain

ARETHA FRANKLIN
Rhythm and Blues Singer, born USA 1942

MARIANNE HAINISCH Educator, born Austria 1839

LOUISE OTTO-PETERS
Feminist Activist, born Germany 1819

26 March 1973
SUSAN SHAW becomes the first woman to set foot on the floor of the London Stock Exchange.

MARCH 27

People who make some other person their job are dangerous.
Dorothy L Sayers, England

_____

_____

_____

_____

_____

MARCH 28

DAME FLORA ROBSON
Actress, born England 1902

_____

_____

_____

_____

_____

Whatever the 'real' differences between the sexes may be, we are not likely to know them until the sexes are treated differently, that is alike.

Kate Millett, USA

PEARL BAILEY
Singer, born USA 1918

ANNA SEWELL
Author (Black Beauty), born England 1820

MARCH *31*

Women hold up half the sky.
Chinese proverb

_____

_____

_____

_____

_____

*Spring is passing and
summer seems to be coming -
the fine white stuff of
apparel spread for drying -
heavenly kaguyama.*

Empress Jito, Japan

April

DEBBIE REYNOLDS (Mary Frances Reynolds)
Singer and Film Actress, born USA 1932

ALEXANDRA KOLLANTAI
Revolutionary Activist and Writer, born Russia 1872

KATHERINE TYNAN
Writer, born Ireland 1861

CATHERINE MACAULAY
Historian, born England 1731

2 April 1914
Cumann na mBan
(Women's counterpart
to the Irish Volunteers)
founded in Ireland.

April *3*

The art of being an artist, if you weren't born in the right place,
is to be able to live through rejections ...

Gabriela Müller, Germany

_____

_____

_____

_____

_____

April *4*

MAYA ANGELOU Writer, born USA 1928

BETTINA VON ARNIM Political Writer, born Germany 1785

_____

_____

_____

4 April 1887
SUSANNA SALTER
becomes the first known
woman mayor in the
world (Argonia, Kansas,
USA).

_____

_____

*I've got a magic charm that I keep up my sleeve. Life doesn't
frighten me at all.*

Maya Angelou, USA

BETTE DAVIS
Film Actress and twice Oscar winner, born USA 1908

5 April 1971
FRAN PHIPPS is the first woman to reach the North Pole.

Surely the world we live in is but the world that lives in us?
Daisy Bates, Ireland

APRIL 7

BILLIE HOLIDAY (Eleanora Holiday)
Jazz and Blues Singer, born USA 1915

GABRIELA MISTRAL (Lucila Godoy Alcayaga)
Poet, born Chile 1889

_____

_____

_____

_____

_____

APRIL 8

MARY PICKFORD (Gladys Marie Smith)
Film Actress, born Canada 1893

DOROTHY TUTIN Actress, born England 1930

SONJA HENIE Olympic Ice Skating Champion, born Norway 1912

_____

_____

_____

_____

_____

I am an instrument in the shape of a woman
trying to translate pulsations into images
for the relief of the body
and the reconstruction of the mind

Adrienne Rich, USA

HELENE LANGE
Feminist Activist, born Germany 1848

_____

_____

_____

_____

9 April 1983
JENNY PITMAN is the
first woman to train an
English Grand National
Steeplechase winner
(Corbiere).

_____

The point of power is in the present moment ... The only thing
we are ever dealing with is a thought, and a thought can be
changed.

Louise L Hay, USA

_____

_____

_____

_____

_____

APRIL *11*

LUISE GOTTSCHED
Writer and Critic, born Germany 1713

APRIL *12*

When a woman loves a woman,
it is the blood of the mothers speaking.

Caribbean proverb

I am colored and wish to be known as colored, but sometimes I have felt that my growth as a writer has been hampered in my own country. And so - but only temporarily - I have fled from it.

Jessie Fauset, USA, writing in Paris in the 1920s

JOSEPHINE BUTLER Social Reformer, born England 1828
EUDORA WELTY Writer, born USA 1909

_____

_____

_____

_____

_____

JULIE CHRISTIE Film Actress and Oscar winner,
born India of British parents 1941

_____

_____

_____

_____

_____

APRIL *15*

BESSIE SMITH
Blues Singer, born USA 1894

_____

_____

_____

_____

_____

APRIL *16*

DUSTY SPRINGFIELD (Mary O'Brien)
Singer, born England 1939

_____

_____

_____

_____

_____

*If you put a bit of love
into ugly things
you'll see that your sadness
will begin to change colour.*

Teresita Fernandez, Cuba

CLARE FRANCIS
Yachtswoman, born England 1946

KAREN BLIXEN (Isak Dinesen)
Writer, born Denmark 1885

LUCREZIA BORGIA
Noblewoman, born Italy 1480

I am a black woman, tall as a cypress ...
Look on me and be renewed.

Mari Evans, USA

APRIL *19*

The present enshrines the past.
Simone de Beauvoir, France

_____

_____

_____

_____

_____

APRIL *20*

BETTY CUTHBERT
Athlete and Sprint Champion, born Australia 1938
SUNITI NAMJOSHI Poet, born India 1941

_____

_____

_____

_____

_____

TAURUS 20 April - 20 May
Element: Earth
Ruler: Venus
Sensual; patient; pleasure oriented; powerful and sensitive;
emotionally mature; great intellectual capacity; trustworthy

CHARLOTTE BRONTË Writer, born England 1816
ANGELA MORTIMER
Tennis Champion, born England 1932

_____

_____

_____

_____

_____

Kartinah Day
(Indonesia)
Kartinah Day is named in honour of the Javanese feminist campaigner and writer, RADEN ADJENG KARTINI, 1879-1904

EVIE HONE Artist, born Ireland 1894
ELLEN GLASGOW Writer, born USA 1874
KATHLEEN FERRIER Concert Singer, born England 1912

_____

_____

_____

_____

_____

Many times have I talked with women, both with those of the nobles and those of the people, about the idea of an independent, free, self-supporting girl, who would earn her own living; and from each comes the answer, there must be someone who sets the example.

Raden Adjeng Kartini, Indonesia

APRIL *23*

SHIRLEY TEMPLE Child Film Star, born USA 1928
GEORGE ANNE BELLAMY Actress, born Ireland 1733

_____

_____

_____

_____

_____

APRIL *24*

SHIRLEY MACLAINE (Shirley Beaty)
Film Actress, born USA 1934
BARBARA STREISAND
Film Actress, born USA 1942

_____

_____

_____

_____

_____

ELLA FITZGERALD Jazz Singer, born USA 1918

Latest date on which
Easter can fall

FANNY BLANKER-KOEN
Athlete, born Holland 1918

EMMA, LADY HAMILTON (Emily Lyon)
born England 1765

Always thinking the moment has arrived.
If not now, then when?

Tracy Chapman, USA

APRIL 27

CORETTA KING (Coretta Scott) Civil Rights Leader, born USA 1927

MARY WOLLSTONECRAFT
Feminist Campaigner and Writer, born England 1759

SHEILA SCOTT Aviator, born England 1927

APRIL 28

You cannot shake hands with a clenched fist.
Indira Ghandi, India

28 April 1915
International Women's
League for Peace and
Freedom founded in The
Hague, Holland.

O daughter, quickened in me by ritual, since you left,
I've been inconsolable at the crossroads.

Citeku Ndaaya, Zaïre

29 April 1884
Oxford University Senate
admits women to University examinations for the
first time.

ALICE B TOKLAS
Writer, born USA 1877

*It is the springtime, as one imagines it in fairy tales, the
exuberant, irresistible springtime of the midi, fat, fresh,
gushing out in tall foliage, in tall grass waving and
shimmering like watered silk in the wind.*

Colette, France

Christian calendar

The Christian calendar includes fixed feasts such as Christmas (25 December) and movable feasts, such as Easter, which vary according to the Moon's phases.

May

MAY *1*

May Day - International Workers' Day
MARIE CORELLI
Romantic Novelist, born England 1855

_____

_____

_____

_____

_____

May Day was the ancient Celtic feast of Bealtaine, Bel/Balder's fire. Effigies of the god were burned to make the crops grow.

MAY *2*

CATHERINE THE GREAT
Empress of Russia, born Germany 1729

_____

_____

_____

_____

_____

MAY *3*

MAY SARTON Novelist and Poet, born Belgium 1912

GOLDA MEIR Israeli Politician
and former Prime Minister, born Russia 1898

MAY *4*

I feel no need for any other faith than my faith in human kind.
Pearl S Buck, USA

---

*Old age is not an illness, it is a timeless ascent. As power
diminshes, we grow towards the light.*
May Sarton, USA

MARY ASTOR (Lucille Langehanke) Film Actress, born USA 1906

ALICE FAYE (Alice Leppert)
Singer and Film Actress, born USA 1915

TAMMY WYNETTE Country and Western Singer, born USA 1942

5 May 1930
AMY JOHNSON sets off from England on the first solo flight from Europe to Australia by a woman.

A slave is a person who is not paid for working.
Sound familiar?

Astra, USA

MAY 7

OLYMPE MARIE de GOUGES Feminist Revolutionary and Author of the 'Declaration of the Rights of Women', born France 1748

7 May 1974
The Three Marias acquitted in Lisbon, Portugal, of outraging public morals and abusing freedom of the press in publishing their book 'New Portuguese Letters'.

MAY 8

We will be victorious if we have not forgotten how to learn.
Rosa Luxemburg, Poland

There's never been a lack of men willing to die bravely. The trouble is to find a few able to live sensibly.
Winifred Holtby, England

GLENDA JACKSON Film Actress and twice Oscar winner,
born England 1936

The first MOTHERS' DAY,
held in the USA by Anna Jarvis, 1907

May *11*

May I see you grey and combing your children's hair.
Irish proverb

May *12*

FLORENCE NIGHTINGALE
Pioneering Nurse, born Italy of English parents 1820

What most of us want is to be heard, to communicate.
Dory Previn, USA

DAPHNE du MAURIER
Novelist, born England 1907

Friday was considered unlucky by early Christians because it was sacred to the goddess Freya and doubly unlucky when it occurred on the thirteenth day of the month since this was her sacred number.

If there had been no priesthood the world would have advanced ten thousand times better than it has now.

Annandabai Joshee,
First Hindu woman to receive a medical degree, 1881

MAY *15*

A word after a word after a word is power.
Margaret Atwood, Canada

_____

_____

_____

_____

_____

MAY *16*

ELIZABETH PEABODY Educator, born USA 1804

OLGA KORBUT Gymnast and Olympic Gold Medallist,
born Russia 1955

_____

_____

_____

16 May 1975
JUNKO TABEI of Japan
is the first woman to _____
reach the summit of
Mount Everest.

Bad moments, like good ones, tend to be grouped together.
Edna O'Brien, Ireland

DOROTHY RICHARDSON Writer, born USA 1873
MAUREEN O'SULLIVAN
Film Actress, born Ireland 1911

MARGOT FONTEYN (Margaret Hookham)
Prima Ballerina, born England 1919

18 May 1953
JACQUELINE COCHRANE
is the first woman to fly faster
than sound.

MAY *19*

DAME NELLIE MELBA (Helen Mitchell)
Operatic Singer, born Australia 1861

LADY ASTOR (Nancy Langhorne)
Politician, born USA 1879

MAY *20*

CHER (Cherilyn La Pierre)
Singer and Actress, born USA 1946

*Those who do not know how to weep with their whole heart
don't know how to laugh either.*

Golda Meir, Israel

ELIZABETH FRY Prison Reformer, born England 1780

AMELIA EARHART is the first woman
to fly the Atlantic solo, 1932

21 May 1908
Women's Suffragette rally of half a million women in Hyde Park with 80 women speakers on 20 platforms all wearing purple, white and green.

SOPHONISBA ANGUISCIOLA
Painter, born Italy 1527

MARY MARIA EDGEWORTH
Writer, born Ireland 1767

SOPHONISBA ANGUISCIOLA, born in Cremona, had five sisters, Europa, Minerva, Lucia, Elena and Anna, each one of whom developed her talents in music, literature or painting.

GEMINI 21 May - 20 June
Element: Air
Ruler: Mercury
Communicator of ideas; versatile; inventive; imaginative;
likes variety and change; mental agility; witty; curious; rebel.

MAY *23*

ROSEMARY CLOONEY Singer, born USA 1928
JOAN COLLINS
Film and Television Actress, born England 1933

International Women's
Day for Disarmament

MAY *24*

SUZANNE LENGLEN Tennis Player and six times
Wimbledon Champion, born France 1899
JOAN HAMMOND Soprano, born New Zealand 1912
SIOBHAN McKENNA Actress, born Ireland 1923

24 MAY 1930
AMY JOHNSON arrives
in Australia on her solo
flight from England in a
Gypsy Moth named
Jason.

JAMAICA KINCAID
Writer, born Jamaica 1949

PEGGY LEE (Norma Egstrom) Singer, born USA 1920
LADY MARY WORTLEY MONTAGU
Writer, born England 1689

For me there is always the rainbow beyond the hill.
Daisy Bates, Ireland

MAY 27

AMELIA BLOOMER
Women's Rights Campaigner, born USA 1818
ISADORA DUNCAN Dancer, born USA 1878
CILLA BLACK (Priscilla White) Singer, born England 1943

MAY 28

GLADYS KNIGHT Soul singer, born USA 1944

World AIDS Day

African Liberation Day

International Day of Action for Women's Health *(Dia de Accion Internacional por la Salud de la Mujer)*

Soon we shall gather in free South Africa with our music, our dance and with our poetry resounding with this simple message 'Amandla!'

Winnie Mandela, South Africa

BEATRICE LILLIE Actress, born Canada 1898

CHRISTINE de PISAN Poet, born France 1364

Feastday of JOAN OF ARC, French military leader burned at the stake for heresy in 1431.

More pain than you, as I maintain, I have had,
But now tell me exactly how many kisses I shall have for it,
For I must know the full account of that.

Christine de Pisan, France

Keep breathing.
Sophie Tucker, USA

Spare no effort, struggle unceasingly,
That at last peace may come to our people ...
And one day, all under heaven
Will see beautiful free women,
Blooming like fields of flowers,
And bearing brilliant and noble human beings.

Ch'iu Chin Revolutionary Leader 1879-1907, China

June

MARILYN MONROE (Norma Jean Baker)
Film Actress, born USA 1926

COLLEEN McCULLOUGH Writer, born Australia 1937

_____

_____

_____

_____

_____

BARBARA PYM
Writer, born England 1913

_____

_____

_____

_____

_____

I have sunk very low.
Today I threw tealeaves out the window.

Barbara Pym, England

JUNE *3*

Am I fact? Or am I fiction? Am I what I know I am?
Or am I what he thinks I am?

Angela Carter, England

JUNE *4*

Ability is sexless.

Christabel Pankhurst, England

I, Jane Hickok Burke, better known as Calamity Jane of my
own free will and being of sound mind do, this June 3, 1903
make this confession. I have lied about my past life ... people
got snoopy so I told them lies to hear their tongues wag!

Martha Jane Burke, 1903

MARGARET DRABBLE
Writer, born England 1939

5 June 1988
KAY COTTEE ended the first solo non-stop round the world voyage by a woman. It took six months.

When the apple is ripe it will fall
Proverb

Autumn arrives in the early morning, but Spring at the close of a winter day.

Elizabeth Bowen, Ireland

JUNE 7

ELIZABETH BOWEN Writer, born Ireland 1899
GWENDOLYN BROOKS Writer, born USA 1917

JUNE 8

MARGUERITE YOURCENAR Writer, born Belgium 1903

8 June 1978
NAOMI JAMES is the
first woman to sail solo
around the world via
Cape Horn, taking 267
days.

*In attempting this ... I know that the total accumulation of
hours and days of this voyage have enriched my life
immeasurably.*

Naomi James, New Zealand

MARCIA DAVENPORT
Writer, born USA 1903

JUDY GARLAND (Frances Ethel Gumm)
Film Actress and Singer, born USA 1922

I was born at the age of twelve on a Metro-Goldwyn Meyer lot.
Judy Garland

June *11*

MARY LAVIN
Writer, born Ireland 11 or 12 June 1912

_____

_____

_____

_____

_____

June *12*

HARRIET MARTINEAU
Writer and Feminist Reformer, born England 1802

_____

_____

_____

_____

_____

*I think it's foolish to determine what your life will be before
you've even had a chance to live it.*

Nikki Giovanni, USA

FANNY BURNEY Writer, born Scotland 1752

DOROTHY L SAYERS Writer, born England 1893

ANNE FRANK Author of 'The Diary of Anne Frank', born Holland 1929

12 June 1893
First Women's Golf Championship took place - won by Margaret Scott.

HARRIET BEECHER STOWE
Writer, born USA 1811

STEFFI GRAF Tennis Player, born Germany 1969

We all live with the objective of being happy; our lives are all different and yet the same.

Anne Frank, The Netherlands

JUNE *15*

I used to be Snow White, but I drifted.
May West, USA

JUNE *16*

JOYCE CAROL OATES
Writer, born USA 1938

---

16 June 1963
VALENTINA
TERESHKOVA, Soviet
cosmonaut, is the first
woman in space, aboard
the Vostok VI

How absurd and delicious it is to be in love with someone younger than yourself. Everyone should try it.

Barbara Pym, England

BERYL REID
Character Actress, born England 1920

EMILY LAWLESS
Writer, born Ireland 1845

EVA BARTOK (Eva Sjoke)
Film Actress, born Hungary 1929

18 June 1983
Dr SALLY RIDE is the
first American woman
in space, on board the
shuttle *Challenger*.

JUNE *19*

Where women are honoured the gods are pleased.
Arab proverb

_____

_____

_____

_____

_____

JUNE *20*

LILLIAN HELLMAN
Writer and Playwright, born USA 1905
CATHERINE COOKSON Novelist, born England 1906
DORIS HART Tennis Champion, born USA 1925

_____

_____

_____

20 June 1960
SHEILA SCOTT, the first
woman to fly solo round _____
the world, arrives back
in England.

*Since when do you have to agree with people to defend them
from injustice?*

Lillian Hellman, USA

BENAZIR BHUTTO Politician, born Pakistan 1953
FRANCOISE SAGAN Writer, born France 1935
MARY McCARTHY Writer and Critic, born USA 1912

Summer Solstice (Northern hemisphere); Winter Solstice (Southern hemisphere).

Midsummer Day, the longest day of the year, was the Festival of the Celtic sun goddess.

MERYL STREEP
Film Actress and Oscar winner, born USA 1949

CANCER 21 June - 22 July
Element: Water
Ruler: Moon
Emotionally sensitive; sympathetic; collector; mentally shrewd; caring; lunar nature; self-protective.

JUNE *23*

ANNIE FRENCH HECTOR (Mrs Alexander)
Writer, born Ireland 1825
WINIFRED HOLTBY Writer, born England 1898

_____

_____

_____

_____

_____

JUNE *24*

A man thinks he knows, but a woman knows better.
Chinese proverb

_____

_____

_____

_____

_____

*I don't see how I can write an autobiography. I never feel I've
really had a life of my own. My existence seems to me like a
clear stream which has simply reflected other people's stories
and lives.*

Winifred Holtby, England

CARLY SIMON
Singer and Composer, born USA 1945

25 June 1903
MARIE CURIE (France)
publishes her discovery
of radium.

PEARL S BUCK
Writer, born USA 1892

Lesbian and Gay Pride
Day (North America)

*Like Confucius of old, I am so absorbed in the wonder of Earth
and the life upon it that I cannot think of heaven and the
angels. I have enough for this life. If there is no other life than
this, this one has been enough to make it worth being born,
myself a human being.*

Pearl S Buck, USA

JUNE *27*

HELEN KELLER
Author and Lecturer, born USA 1880

27 June 1693
'The Ladies' Mercury'
appears, the first
women's magazine to
be published in England.

JUNE *28*

A man who betrays a woman
had best sleep with one eye open.

Japanese proverb

*Many persons have a wrong idea of what constitutes true
happiness. It is not obtained through self-gratification, but
through fidelity to a worthy purpose.*

Helen Keller, 1938

... As a woman I have no country.
As a woman I want no country.

Virginia Woolf, England

SUSAN HAYWARD (Edythe Marriner)
Film Actress and Oscar winner, born USA 1919

LENA HORNE Singer, born USA 1917

You see, I have survived so long,
my habit of observation grown so strong
that sometimes I think I almost belong.

Suniti Namjoshi, India

Hebrew calendar
The Hebrew calendar is based on the Moon, usually with 12 months, alternately 30 and 29 days long.

July

JULY *1*

GEORGE SAND (Amandine Dupin)
Writer, born France 1804

AMY JOHNSON Aviator, born England 1903

JULY *2*

NAOMI JACOB
Traveller and Writer, born New Zealand 1884

2 July 1928
Women in Britain obtain
the vote on same basis
as men.

The old woman I shall become is quite different from the woman I am now. Another I is beginning.

George Sand, France

JULY 3

ELIZABETH TAYLOR
Novelist, born England 1912

_____

_____

_____

_____

_____

JULY 4

GINA LOLLOBRIGIDA
Film Actress, born Italy 1928

PAM SHRIVER
Tennis Player, born USA 1962

_____

_____

_____

_____

_____

CLARA ZETKIN
Socialist Activist, born Germany 1857

FRANCOISE MALLET-JORIS Writer, born France 1930

*By the time your life is finished, you will have learned just
enough to begin it well.*

Eleanor Marx, 1855-1898 UK

JULY 7

One swallow never made a summer
Proverb

JULY 8

KÄTHE KOLLWITZ
Artist, born Germany 1867

*I do not want to die ... until I have faithfully made the most of
my talent and cultivated the seed that was placed in me until
the last small twig has grown.*

Käthe Kollwitz, Germany

BARBARA CARTLAND
Romantic Novelist, born England 1901

ANN RADCLIFFE Novelist, born England 1764

9 July 1956
20,000 women marched on Pretoria, South Africa, to protest against the extension of the iniquitous pass law system to women, a system aimed at controlling Black migrant labourers.

VIRGINIA WADE
Tennis Player, born England 1945

10 July 1985
The closing conference for the UN Decade for Women opened in Nairobi, Kenya.

July *11*

Occupation is essential.
Virginia Woolf

_____
_____
_____
_____
_____

July *12*

KIRSTEN FLAGSTAD
Singer, born Norway 1895

_____
_____
_____
_____
_____

What would happen if one woman told the truth about her life? The world would split open.
Muriel Rukeyser, USA

Muslim New Year occurs on this day in 1991 (Year 1412),
on 2 July in 1992, on 21 June in 1993.

_____

_____

_____

_____

_____

EMMELINE PANKHURST (Emmeline Goulden)
Suffragette, born England 1858

_____

_____

_____

_____

_____

I am what you call a hooligan!
Emmeline Pankhurst, England

JULY *15*

IRIS MURDOCH Writer, born Ireland 1919
LINDA RONSTADT Singer, born USA 1946

JULY *16*

MARY BAKER EDDY Founder of Christian Science
Movement, born USA 1821

GINGER ROGERS (Virginia Katherine McMath)
Dancer and Film Actress, born USA 1911

MARGARET COURT
(Margaret Smith) Tennis
Player, born Australia
1942.

They're talkin' about a revolution.
It sounds like a whisper.

Tracy Chapman, USA

CHRISTINA STEAD
Writer, born Australia 1902

SHIRLEY STRICKLAND
Olympic Athlete, born Australia 1925

*Obviously we have to take responsibility
for our own survival ...*
Huma Ibrahim, Pakistan

JULY *19*

God is love but get it in writing.
Gypsy Rose Lee

19 July 1848
The first ever Women's
Right Convention was
held at Seneca Falls, New
York State, USA.

JULY *20*

NATALIE WOOD (Natasha Gurdin)
Film Actress, born USA 1938

The common woman is as common as the best of bread
and will rise.

Judy Grahn, USA

21 July 1960
SIRIMAVO
BANDARANAIKE is
elected Prime Minister
of Ceylon - the first
woman in the world to
hold Prime Ministerial
office.

Domestic Work Day *(Dia del Trabajo Domestico)*
EMMA LAZARUS Writer, born USA 1849

22 July 1849
EMMA LAZARUS, who
wrote the poem en-
graved on the pedestal
of the Statue of Liberty,
was born in New York,
the daughter of Jewish
immigrant parents.

Send these, the homeless, tempest-tossed to me
I lift my lamp beside the golden door.

Emma Lazarus, USA

July *23*

ZELDA SYRE FITZGERALD born USA, 1900

July *24*

AMELIA EARHART
Aviator, born USA 1898

LEO 23 July - 22 August
Element: Fire
Ruler: Sun
Self-expressive; energetic; spontaneous and extrovert; loyal;
show woman; dignified; generous and magnanimous.

Life does not need to mutilate itself in order to be pure.
Simone Weil, France

_____

_____

_____

_____

_____

If you haven't got anything nice to say about anyone,
come sit by me.
Alice Roosevelt Longworth, USA

_____

_____

_____

_____

26 July 1565
First Witch trial in
England begins at
Chelmsford, Essex.

JULY *27*

SHIRLEY WILLIAMS
Politican, born England 1930

_____

_____

_____

_____

_____

JULY *28*

BEATRIX POTTER Author
and Illustrator of children's books, born England 1866

_____

_____

_____

_____

_____

It is a long baptism into the seas of humankind, my daughter.
Better immersion than to live untouched.

Tillie Olsen, USA

To keep a lamp burning we have to keep putting oil in it.
Mother Theresa of Calcutta

EMILY BRONTË
Novelist, born England 1818

JULY *31*

---

*The Muses have made me happy
in my lifetime*

*and when I die
I shall never be forgotten*

Sappho, Greece

August

Lammas Day / Feast of Lughnasa

MYRNA LOY (Myrna Williams)
Film Actress, born USA 1905

AUGUST *3*

PD JAMES Crime Fiction Writer,
born England 1920

AUGUST *4*

MARY DECKER
Athlete, born USA 1958

I am told I must modestly cast down my eyes. I will not do
that. I will look at men, as well as women, straight in the eye,
not cast down my own before them.

Raden Adjeng Kartini, Java

JOAN HICKSON Actress, born England 1906

LUCILLE BALL
Film Actress, born USA 1911

Hiroshima Day
Anniversary of the first
Bomb attack in 1945

*The 6th August 1945 - which I don't forget - the things that
happened this day are deeply carved in my heart.*
Takako Okimoto, Japan

AUGUST 7

MATA HARI (Margarete Gertrude Zelle)
Dancer, born Holland 1876

ELIZABETH GURLEY FLYNN
Labour Organiser, born Ireland 1890

ELIZABETH GURLEY FLYNN was an Irish-American labour activist and travelling organiser for the 'International Workers of the World' who was jailed many times for her work.

AUGUST 8

CONNIE STEVENS (Concetta Ingolia)
Singer, born USA 1938

ESTHER WILLIAMS Swimmer, born USA 1923

AUGUST *9*

South African Women's Day
Nagasaki Day

Anniversary of the
second Atomic Bomb
attack in 1945.

AUGUST *10*

This woman is so dynamic, she will make the birds sing
and the trees rustle wherever she goes.

Anne Benjamin writing of Winnie Mandela

*Now you have touched women; now you have struck a rock;
now you have dislodged a boulder, now you will be crushed.*

South African Women's Freedom Song

AUGUST *11*

ENID BLYTON
Author of children's books, born England 1897

_____

_____

_____

_____

_____

AUGUST *12*

Oh no you can't! Oh yes I can!
Helen McNeil, England

_____

_____

_____

_____

_____

LUCY STONE Feminist Social Reformer, born USA 1818

THEROIGNE de MERICOURT
Revolutionary Fighter, born France 1762

ANNIE OAKLEY (Phoebe Anne Oakley Mozee)
Crack Rifle Shot and Entertainer, born USA 1860

THEROIGNE de MERICOURT who was known as 'The Amazon of Freedom'. She fought in the storming of the Bastille in Paris in 1789.

Women like to sit down with trouble as if it were knitting.
Ellen Glasgow, USA

AUGUST *15*

ETHEL BARRYMORE (Ethel Blythe)
Singer and Actress, born USA 1879

EDNA FERBER Writer and Journalist, born USA 1887

_____

_____

_____

_____

_____

AUGUST *16*

MADONNA (Madonna Louise Veronica Ciccone)
Singer and Actress, born USA 1958

_____

_____

_____

_____

_____

*Woman's work! Housework's the hardest work in the world.
That's why men won't do it.*

Edna Ferber, USA

AUGUST *17*

MAE WEST Film Actress, born USA 1892

MAUREEN O'HARA (Maureen Fitzsimmons)
Film Actress, born Ireland 1921

AUGUST *18*

ELSA MORANTE Writer, born Italy 1918

SHELLY WINTERS, (Shirley Schrift)
Film Actress, born USA 1922

18 August 1960
Birth Control Pill
launched in America.

Too much of a good thing can be wonderful.
Mae West, USA

AUGUST *19*

COCO CHANEL (Gabriella Chanel)
Fashion Designer, born France 1883

AUGUST *20*

The hand that rocks the cradle can also rock the boat.

You need double strength if you quarrel
with an independent woman.

Shona saying, Zimbabwe

DOROTHY PARKER
Poet and Woman of Letters, born USA 1893

They say of me, and so they should,
It's doubtful if I come to good.

Dorothy Parker, USA

August *23*

I love all of my children. Some of them I don't like.
Lilian Carter, USA

_____

_____

_____

_____

_____

August *24*

JEAN RHYS
Writer, born Dominica, West Indies 1894

_____

_____

_____

_____

_____

VIRGO 23 August - 22 September
Element: Earth
Ruler: Mercury
Seeker of knowledge; analytical; self-reliant; meticulous;
practical; constructive; sign of a healer.

ALTHEA GIBSON
Tennis Champion, born USA 1927

Women in the USA gained the right to vote, 1920

On 26 August, 1970, a group of women calling themselves the Emma Goldman Brigade marched down Fifth Avenue in New York City with many other feminists, chanting: 'Emma said it in 1910. Now we're going to say it again.'
(*Christie V McDonald*, 1982)

It is a time of hate
and I am nowhere brave ...

Eithne Strong, Ireland

AUGUST *27*

MOTHER THERESA OF CALCUTTA
born Yugoslavia 1910

_____

_____

_____

_____

_____

AUGUST *28*

If living makes women crazy, then living is crazy.
Marge Piercy, USA

_____

_____

_____

_____

_____

The dream is real, my friends.
The failure to make it work is the unreality.
Toni Cade Bambara, USA

INGRID BERGMAN
Film Actress and Oscar winner, born Sweden 1915

DINAH WASHINGTON (Ruth Jones)
Blues Singer, born USA 1924

_____

_____

_____

_____

_____

MARY SHELLEY
Writer, born England 1797

_____

_____

_____

_____

_____

One day life will be flooded with sun.
And it will be like a new childhood shining for everyone ...

Noemia da Sousa, Mozambique

Beauty is everlasting,
And dust is for a time.

Marianne Moore, USA

Love must not crush the woman's individuality, nor bind her wings. If love begins to ensnare her, she must make herself free, she must step over all love tragedies, and go her own way.

Alexendra Kollontai, Russia

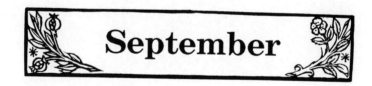

September

VIOLET CARSON
Actress and Pianist, born England 1905

YVONNE DE CARLO (Peggy Middleton)
Film Actress, born Canada 1924

Women are all one nation.

Turkish saying

SEPTEMBER *3*

SARAH ORNE JEWETT
Feminist Reformer, born USA 1849

_____

_____

_____

_____

_____

SEPTEMBER *4*

Only in romantic novels are the beautiful guaranteed
happiness.

Cynthia Asquith, England

_____

_____

_____

_____

_____

If you don't like my ocean
Don't fish in my sea
Stay out of my valley
And let my mountain be.

Ma Rainey, USA

HENRIETTE HERZ
Writer and Critic, born Germany 1764

Wisdom never kicks at the iron walls it can't bring down.
Olive Schreiner, South Africa

September 7

QUEEN ELIZABETH 1 of England, born England 1533

7 September 1838
GRACE DARLING rescues the crew of the 'Forfarshire', wrecked in heavy seas off the English coast.

September 8

In the face of an obstacle which it is impossible to overcome, stubborness is stupid.

Simone de Beauvoir, France

International Literacy Day

Right now the sweet white bush clover is blooming, but sooner or later winter will come, and the flowers and the stems will dry up. Just wait and see.

Hayashi Fumiko, Japan

Jewish New Year occurs on this day in 1991 (Year 5752),
on 28 September in 1992, on 16 September in 1993.

_____

_____

_____

_____

_____

A woman is more crafty than a king.
Hausa saying, Nigeria

_____

_____

_____

_____

_____

September *11*

'Progress' affects few. Only revolution can affect many.
Alice Walker, USA

September *12*

When you are carrying on a struggle, you have to accept the
notion that you will have enemies.
Francoise Giroud, France

*Each day and the living of it has to be a conscious creation in
which discipline and order are relieved with some play and
some pure foolishness.*

May Sarton, USA

CLAUDETTE COLBERT (Lily Claudette Chauchoin)
Film Actress and Oscar winner, born France 1905

_____

_____

_____

_____

_____

KATE MILLET Writer and Feminist Activist, born USA 1934
ALICE MILLIGAN Writer, born Ireland 1866

_____

_____

_____

_____

_____

SEPTEMBER *15*

AGATHA CHRISTIE
Detective Story Writer, born England 1890

_____

_____

_____

_____

_____

SEPTEMBER *16*

LAUREN BACALL (Betty Joan Perske)
Film Actress, born USA 1924

_____

_____

_____

_____

_____

But Jesus, you can't start worrying about what's GOING to happen. You get frantic enough worrying about what's happening now.

Lauren Bacall, USA

MAUREEN CONNOLLY (Little Mo)
Tennis Player, born USA 1934

_____

_____

_____

_____

_____

Yom Kippur (Day of Atonement) occurs on this day in 1991,
on 7 October in 1992, on 25 September in 1993.

GRETA GARBO (Greta Lovisa Gustafsson)
Film Actress, born Sweden 1905

_____

_____

_____

_____

_____

SEPTEMBER *19*

TWIGGY (Lesley Hornby)
Actress and Model, born England 1949

19 September 1893
New Zealand women
are the first to gain the
right to vote.

SEPTEMBER *20*

SOPHIA LOREN (Sophia Scicoloni)
Actress and Oscar winner, born Italy 1934

NORAH HOULT Writer, born Ireland 1896

STEVIE SMITH Poet, born England 1902

*I try to make family life so gorgeous - not hatred and linoleum
- but warmth and hydrangeas.*

Katherine Mansfield, New Zealand

Autumn is a weather-cock
Blown every way ...

Christina Rossetti, England

Autumnal Equinox
(when day and night are
of equal length)

CHRISTABEL PANKHURST
Suffragette, born England 1880

FAY WELDON Novelist, born England 1933

Remember the dignity of your womanhood. Do not appeal, do not beg, do not grovel. Take courage, join hands, stand beside us, fight with us.

Christabel Pankhurst, England

SEPTEMBER *23*

BARONESS ORCSY
Author of 'The Scarlet Pimpernel', born Hungary 1865
VICTORIA WOODHULL Sugffragette, born USA 1838

VICTORIA WOODHULL was the first woman to stand as a presidential candidate in the USA.

SEPTEMBER *24*

EAVAN BOLAND Poet, born Ireland 1944

LIBRA 23 September - 23 October
Element: Air
Ruler: Venus
Charm and grace in expression; mediator; lover of beauty;
strong sense of justice; idealistic; socialiser; inspirational;
organiser.

FELICIA HEMANS (Felicia Dorothea Browne)
Poet, born England 1793

25 September 1981
SANDRA O'CONNOR
takes her seat as the first
woman justice of the
USA Supreme Court

MARINA IVANOVNA TSVETAYEVA
Poet, born Russia 1892

A new language
is a kind of scar
And heals after a while
into a passable imitation
of what went before.

Eavan Boland, Ireland

September *27*

The great task in life is to find reality.
Iris Murdoch, Ireland

27 September 1904
A woman is arrested in
New York city for
smoking a cigarette in a
taxi cab.

September *28*

ALICE MARBLE Tennis player, born USA 1913

28 September 1865
ELIZABETH GARRETT
ANDERSON is the first
British woman to register
as a surgeon and physic-
ian.

*What I enjoy most in my works is the laughter and the
outrage and the attention to language. I come from a family of
very gifted laughers.*
Toni Cade Bambara, USA

ELIZABETH GASKELL (Elizabeth Stevenson)
Writer, born England 1810

GREER GARSON
Film Actress and Oscar winner, born Ireland 1908

ELLSWORTH VINES Tennis Champion, born USA 1911

DEBORAH KERR Film Actress, born Scotland 1921

When my bones are stiff and aching
And my feet won't climb the stairs,
I will only ask one favour:
Don't bring me no rocking chair.

Maya Angelou, USA

BABYLONIAN CALENDAR
The Babylonian calendar was based on the 354-day lunar year.

ROMAN CALENDAR
The Roman calendar was based on a 304-day year divided into 10 months: Martius, Aprilis, Maius, Junius, Quintilis, Sextilis, September, October, November and December.

ANNA LUISE KARSCH
Poet, known as the 'German Sappho', born Prussia 1722
BONNIE PARKER
Outlawed with her partner, Clyde, born USA 1910

I'm as pure as the driven slush.
Tallulah Bankhead, USA

OCTOBER *3*

A woman's heart sees more than ten mens' eyes.
Swedish proverb

_____

_____

_____

_____

_____

OCTOBER *4*

Success is counted sweetest by those who ne'er succeed.
Emily Dickinson, USA

_____

_____

_____

_____

_____

Each time you love
love as deeply
as if it were
forever
only nothing is
eternal.

Audre Lord, USA

October *5*

DIANE CILENTO
Film Actress, born Australia 1933

5 October 1936
ELLEN WILKINSON,
MP, leads the Jarrow
March of the Unemploy-
ed to London.

October *6*

JENNY LIND (Johanna Maria Lind)
Soprana, born Sweden 1820

HELEN WILLS-MOODY Tennis Player, born USA 1905

OCTOBER 7

JUNE ALLYSON (Ella Geisman)
Film Actress, born USA 1923

_____

_____

_____

_____

_____

OCTOBER 8

EDITH SOMERVILLE Novelist, born Ireland 1858

_____

_____

_____

_____

_____

*My imagination takes me to so many places - it flies, and I fly
with it. I am happiest of all when I am working, when I am
writing.*

Natalya Baranskaya, Russia

Men are mountains and women are the levers that move them.

Pushtu proverb, Afghanistan

_____

_____

_____

_____

_____

HELEN HAYES (Helen Brown)
Actress and Oscar winner, born USA 1900

DOROTHY LAMOUR (Dorothy Kaumeyer)
Actress, born USA 1914

_____

_____

_____

_____

_____

One day the fields will be forever green
and the earth will be black, sweet and moist.
Our children will grow tall on her
And the children of our children

Daisy Yamora, Nicaragua

OCTOBER *11*

MARIA BUENO
Tennis Player, born Brazil 1939

ELEANOR ROOSEVELT
Humanitarian and Journalist, born USA 1884

_____

_____

_____

_____

_____

_____

OCTOBER *12*

EMMA GRAF
Women's Rights Activist, born Switzerland 1865

_____

_____

_____

_____

_____

No one can make you feel inferior without your consent.
Eleanor Roosevelt, USA

LILLIE LANGTRY (Emilie Charlotte)
Actress, born Jersey 1853

KATHERINE MASNFIELD Writer, born New Zealand 1888
HANNAH ARENDT Philosopher, born Austria 1906

To expect truth to come from thinking signifies that we mistake the need to think with the urge to know.

Hannah Arendt, Austria

OCTOBER *15*

MARIE STOPES
Scientist and Sex Education Reformer, born Scotland 1880

MARGARET BURKE SHERIDAN ('Divine Diva')
Soprano, born Ireland 1889

OCTOBER *16*

ANGELA LANSBURY
Actress, born England 1925

Weapon or spirit
enemy or friend
how a world begins
is how a world will end.

Dory Previn, USA

Life is too important to be serious.
Rita Mae Brown, USA

MARTINA NAVRATILOVA
Tennis Champion, born Czechoslovakia 1956
PEG WOFFINGTON Actress, born Ireland c.1780

Women have moved on from demanding equal opportunity
and now demand equal power.
Andrea Dworkin, USA

OCTOBER *19*

There is nothing new except that which is forgotten.

Mademoiselle Bertin, France

OCTOBER *20*

And you must know this now
I, me, I am a free black woman.

Christine Craig, Jamaica

Women never have young minds. They are born three thousand years old.

Shelagh Delaney, England

Things to be grateful for ...
Not being a horsechestnut in Autumn.

Eleanor Bron, England

_____

_____

_____

_____

_____

SARAH BERNHARDT (Henriette Rosine Bernard)
Actress, born France 1844

DORIS LESSING Writer, born South Africa 1919

_____

_____

_____

_____

_____

*My mother's Welsh intensity and lyric feeling for nature were
not just the air that I breathed but, surely, were in the body
that I breathed with.*

Denise Levertov

OCTOBER 23

GERTRUDE EDERLE
First woman to swim the English Channel, born USA 1906

_____

_____

_____

_____

23 October 1976
Women went on a one-
day strike in Iceland.

OCTOBER 24

DENISE LEVERTOV Poet, born England 1923
SYBIL THORNDIKE
Stage and Film Actress, born England 1882

_____

_____

_____

United Nations Day

24 October 1929
VIRGINIA WOOLF'S 'A
Room of One's Own'
published in England.

SCORPIO 24 October - 21 November
Element: Water
Ruler: Pluto and Mars
Intense in expression and feeling; strong willed; generous;
passionate; purposeful; strong reasoning power; subtle;
determined.

HELEN REDDY
Singer and Songwriter, born Australia 1941

Language is magic - it makes things appear and disappear.
Nicole Brossard, Canada

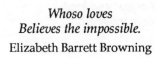

Whoso loves
Believes the impossible.
Elizabeth Barrett Browning

OCTOBER 27

SYLVIA PLATH
Writer, born USA 1932

_____

_____

_____

_____

_____

OCTOBER 28

No one sleeps in this room without the dream
of a common language.

Adrienne Rich, USA

_____

_____

_____

_____

_____

Mother, mother, what illbred aunt
Or what disfigured and unsightly
Cousin did you so unwisely keep
unasked to my christening, that she
Sent these ladies in her stead
With heads like darning-eggs to nod
And nod and nod at foot and head
And at the left side of my crib?

Sylvia Plath, USA

FANNY BRICE
Singer and Comedienne, born USA 1891

If youth did not matter so much to itself
it would never have the heart to go on.

Willa Cather, USA

I do not refer to myself as a "housewife"
for the reason that I did not marry a house.

Wilma Scott Heide, USA

October *31*

SARAH ALLGOOD
Actress, born Ireland 1883

_____

_____

_____

_____

_____

Hallowe'en

Wind moving through grass so that the grass quivers.
This moves me with an emotion I don't even understand.

Katherine Mansfield, New Zealand

November

The winter trees are musical.
Gwendolyn Brooks, USA

MARIE ANTOINETTE
Queen of France, born Austria 1755

---

*I am going to talk several times while I am here; so now I will
do a little singing. I have not heard any singing since I came
here.*

Sojourner Truth, USA

NOVEMBER 3

We are women who come from a place
almost incredible in its beauty ...
Michelle Cliff, Jamaica

_____

_____

_____

_____

_____

NOVEMBER 4

LADY ROSINA LYTTON
Actress, born Ireland 1802

_____

_____

_____

_____

_____

ELLA WHEELER WILCOX
Feminist Activist and Writer, born USA 1850

VIVIEN LEIGH (Vivien Hartley)
Film Actress, born India of English parents 1913

If you stay in the mainstream
you are likely to end up in a backwater.

Ursula Le Guin, USA

Give us that grand word 'woman' once again,
And let's have done with 'lady'; one's a term
Full of fine force, strong, beautiful, and firm,
Fit for the noblest use of tongue or pen;
And one's a word for lackeys.

Ella Wheeler Wilcox, USA

NOVEMBER 7

MARIE CURIE (Marie Sklodowska)
Scientist, born Poland 1867

JOAN SUTHERLAND Soprano, born Australia 1926

CHRYSTOS Poet, born USA 1946

NOVEMBER 8

MARGARET MITCHELL
Author of 'Gone with the Wind', born USA 1900

ANNE SEXTON Poet, born USA 1928

MARIE DRESSLER (Lelia Von Koerber)
Actress, born Canada 1869

KATHARINE
HEPBURN Film Actress
and Oscar winner, born
USA 1909

HEDY LAMARR
(Hedwig Kiesler) Film
actress, born Austria 1915

I am myself struggling towards myself.
Donna Kate Rushin, USA

*Working together as women ... we can challenge and inspirit
each other, throw light on one another's blind spots, stand by
and give courage at the birth throes of one another's insights.*
Adrienne Rich, USA

NOVEMBER *11*

We don't want revenge. We want promotion.
Sadie Roberts, England

_____
_____
_____
_____
_____

NOVEMBER *12*

ELIZABETH CADY STANTON
Feminist Activist and Writer, born USA 1815

NADIA COMANECI
Champion Gymnast, born Romania 1961

_____
_____
_____
_____
_____

Woman will always be dependent until she holds a purse of her own.

Elizabeth Cady Stanton, USA

I was taught that the way of progress is neither swift nor easy.

Marie Curie, France

13 November 1914
The bra was patented by
MARY JANE PHELPS in
the USA.

VERONICA LAKE (Constance Ockleman)
Film Actress, born USA 1919

14 November 1983
First Cruise missiles
arrive at Greenham
Common, Berkshire.

free me
free me
the people are calling
South Africa, are you listening?

Zinzi Mandela, South Africa

NOVEMBER 15

CHARLOTTE MEW Writer, born England 1869
MARIANNE MOORE Poet, born USA 1887
GEORGIA O'KEEFE Artist, born USA 1887

NOVEMBER 16

Surviving meant being born over and over.
Erica Jong, USA

16 November 1987
DIANE ABBOT, the only
black woman ever to be
elected a Member of
Parliament, makes her
first speech in West-
minster.

Where I was born and where and how I have lived are
unimportant. It is what I have done with where I have been
that should be of interest.

Georgia O'Keefe, USA

ELIZABETH 1 accedes to the throne of England, 1558

_____

_____

_____

_____

_____

Opinions differ most when there is least
scientific evidence for having any.

Daisy Bates, Ireland

_____

_____

_____

_____

_____

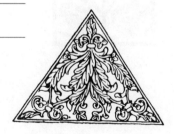

I would rather be a beggar and single than a queen and married.

Elizabeth 1 of England

NOVEMBER *19*

INDIRA GHANDI
First Woman Prime Minister of India, born India 1917

NOVEMBER *20*

NADINE GORDIMER Novelist, born South Africa 1923
SELMA LAGERLOF Writer, born Sweden 1858

If you're small you better be a winner.
Billie Jean King, USA

MARILYN FRENCH
Writer, born USA 1929

BILLIE-JEAN KING Tennis Champion, born USA 1943
GEORGE ELIOT Novelist, born England 1819

22 November 1909
Uprising of 20,000 wo-
men garment-makers in
New York.

SAGITTARIUS 22 November - 21 December
Element: Fire
Ruler: Jupiter
Lover of liberty and freedom; vast and inspirational mind;
optimistic; adventurous; energetic; sincere;
constant desire to expand through ideals.

NOVEMBER *23*

One cannot always be laughing at a man without now and
then stumbling on something witty.

Jane Austen, England

NOVEMBER *24*

All things that pass
Are wisdom's looking-glass.

Christina Rossetti, England

Thanksgiving (USA)

Let me humbly say
Thank you for this day
I want to thank you.

Maya Angelou, USA

International Women's Day of Non-Violence
(Dia de la No Violencia contra la Mujer)

_____

_____

_____

_____

_____

Life comes a hurrying,
Or life lags slow;
But you've stopped worrying -
Let it go!

Dorothy Parker, USA

_____

_____

_____

_____

_____

*If we had keen vision and feeling of all ordinary human life, it
would be like hearing the grass grow and the squirrel's heart
beat, and we should die of that roar which lies on the other side
of silence.*

George Eliot, England

NOVEMBER *27*

GAIL SHEEHY Writer, born USA 1933

NOVEMBER *28*

MARIE BASHKIRTSEFF Writer, born Russia 1858

To die is a word which is easily said and written, but to think, to believe *that one is going to die soon? Do I really* believe *it? No, but I fear it.*

Marie Bashkirtseff, Russia

LOUISA MAY ALCOTT Writer, born USA 1832

VIRGINIA MAYO (Virginia Jones)
Film Actress, born USA 1920

I sing you sunrise
and love
and someone to touch.

Mari Evans, USA

Islamic calendar
The Islamic calendar is based on a 354-day lunar year, with
12 months of 30 and 29 days alternately.

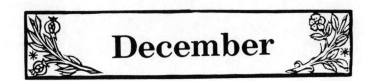

December

DECEMBER *1*

ALICIA MARKOVA (Lilian Alicia Marks)
Prima Ballerina, born England 1910

1 December 1919
Lady Astor is the first
woman to sit in the
British Parliament at
Westminster.

DECEMBER *2*

Even if it ultimately kills you, you'll have been alive and we all
have to die, even those who never lived.

Winifred Holtby, England

DECEMBER *3*

KATE O'BRIEN
Writer, born Ireland 1897

_____

_____

_____

_____

_____

DECEMBER *4*

EDITH CAVELL Nurse, born England 1865
DEANNA DURBIN
Singer and actress, born Canada 1922

_____

_____

_____

_____

_____

*We are a tongued folk, a race of singers. Our lips shape words
and rythms which elevate our spirits and quicken our blood.*

Maya Angelou, USA

JOAN DIDION Novelist and Journalist, born USA 1934
CHRISTINA ROSSETTI Poet, born England 1830

_____

_____

_____

_____

_____

Women are the real architects of society.
Harriet Beecher Stowe, USA

_____

_____

_____

_____

_____ Greenham Women's
Peace Camp Day

December 7

WILLA CATHER
Writer, born USA 1873

December 8

MARY QUEEN OF SCOTS, born Scotland 1542

ELIZABETH SCHWARZKOPF
Operatic Singer, born Germany 1915

EMILY DICKINSON
Poet, born USA 1830

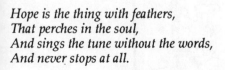

Hope is the thing with feathers,
That perches in the soul,
And sings the tune without the words,
And never stops at all.

Emily Dickinson, USA

DECEMBER *11*

GRACE PALEY Novelist, born USA 1922
ELLEN KEY Educator and Writer, born Sweden 1849

DECEMBER *12*

CONNIE FRANCIS Singer, born USA 1938
DIONNE WARWICK Singer, born USA 1941

Happiness is like a sunbeam
which the least shadow intercepts.

Chinese proverb

_____

_____

_____

_____

_____

People with bad consciences
always fear the judgement of children.

Mary McCarthy, USA

_____

_____

_____

_____

14 December 1918
Women aged 30 and over
are eligible to vote in a
British General Election
for the first time.

DECEMBER *15*

EDNA O'BRIEN Novelist, born Ireland 1930
MURIEL RUKEYSER Poet, born USA 1913

I'm an Irish catholic and I have a long iceberg of guilt.
Edna O'Brien, Ireland

DECEMBER *16*

MARGARET MEAD Anthropologist, born England 1901
JANE AUSTEN Novelist, born England 1775

Single women have a dreadful propensity to being poor.
Jane Austen, England

Many years back a woman of strong purpose passed through
this section and everything else tried to follow.

Judy Grahn, USA

BETTY GRABLE
Film Actress, born USA 1916

18 December 1970
Divorce became legal in
Italy.

*I've got two reasons for success and I'm standing on both of
them.*

Betty Grable, USA

DECEMBER *19*

Dr ANN BISHOP
Pioneer in the fight against Malaria, born England 1899

DECEMBER *20*

IRENE DUNNE Film Actress, born USA 1904

MAUD GONNE MacBRIDE
Revolutionary, born England 1865

We can never go back again, that much is certain.
Daphne du Maurier, England

JANE FONDA Film actress, born USA 1937
CHRISTINE EVERT Tennis player, born USA 1954

Winter Solstice
(Northern hemisphere);
Summer Solstice
(Southern hemisphere)

You can do two things, just shut up, which is something I
don't find very easy, or learn an awful lot very fast, which is
what I tried to do.

Jane Fonda, USA

CAPRICORN 22 December - 21 January
Element: Earth. Ruler: Saturn
Excellent intuition; deep spiritual understanding; resourceful;
disciplined; reliable; self-sufficient; creative.

DECEMBER 23

My dream is to ride the tempest, tame the waves, kill the sharks. I want to drive the enemy away to save our people. I will not accept the usual fate of women who bow their heads and become concubines.

Trieu Thi Vinh, Vietnam

DECEMBER 24

AVA GARDNER (Lucy Johnson)
Film Actress, born USA 1922

Modranet/
Christmas Eve
This day was once called Modranet, the night of the Mother, and celebrated as a greater festival than Christmas Day.

REBECCA WEST (Cicely Isabel Fairfield)
Writer, born Ireland 1892

CLARA BARTON Humanitarian, born USA 1821

Christmas Day

Radium discovered and isolated by Marie Curie, 1898

I myself have never been able to find out precisely what feminism is: I only know that people call me a feminist whenever I express sentiments that differentiate me from a doormat.

Rebecca West, Ireland

DECEMBER *27*

MARLENE DIETRICH (Marie Magdalena von Losch)
Film Actress, born Germany 1901

27 December 1975
Sex Discrimination &
Equal Pay Act came into
force in Britain.

DECEMBER *28*

MAGGIE SMITH
Film Actress and Oscar winner, born England 1934

VERA BRITTAIN
Writer, Feminist and Pacifist, born England 1893

_____

_____

_____

_____

_____

I found god in myself
and I loved her
fiercely.

Ntozake Shange, USA

_____

_____

_____

_____

_____

When one loves deeply it is almost impossible to remember
what the time was like before one did.

Vera Brittain, England

DECEMBER *31*

This is a good time
This is the best time
This is the only time to come together ...

June Jordan, USA

Yes, I am wise, but it's wisdom full of pain
Yes, I've paid the price, but look how much I've gained
I am Wise, I am Invincible, I am Woman.

Helen Reddy, Australia